The CHRISTMAS Family Tree

A Children's Musical by
Kathie Hill

Created and Written by Kathie Hill
Arranged and Recorded by Chris Marion & John DeVries
Music Engraving by Allan Tuten, Compute-A-Chart, Nashville, Tennessee

Recorded at Hilltop Studios, Broadvision, Abtracks Studios
Engineers: Brent King, Glen Spinner, Kevin Ward, Bill Warner, Ed Sharp

Design Editor and Executive Producer: Cherry G. Tadlock,
Dovetail Music (a division of Genevox)

COMPANION PRODUCTS:

Promo Pak 07673 3284 9

Listening Cassette 07673 3281 4

Accompaniment Cassette 07673 3280 6
SIDE A: Split track (Voices right: Instruments left)
Side B: Stereo (instruments only)

Accompaniment CD 07673 3279 2
Split-track and Stereo Tracks

Dovetailor 07673 3283 0

Video (Instructional) 07673 3400 0
Providing suggestions for movement,
costuming and staging

A division of Genevox

07673 3282 2

A Word from the Author

What's happening next door to Abbie Adams? Her new neighbors, the Christmases, are celebrating the holiday season with their annual family tree-trimming party. When she is invited to join the festivities, Abbie is introduced not only to the members of *that* Christmas family, but to key members of the *original* Christmas family. Through this Christmas family tree, Abbie learns of Rahab's bravery, Ruth's loyalty, David's repentance, Josiah's wisdom, and Mary and Joseph's obedience. But, most important, Abbie learns that shee, too, can be adopted into the Christmas family of faith.

Kathie Hill is the creator of *The Christmas Family Tree* as well as *Holly Day's Songs of Praise, Nic at Night, Amerikids, Christmas in Egypt, Go, Go, Jonah!* and *The Don't Be Afraid Brigade,* all available through Genevox Music.

Sequence

4

Setting

Present day Adamsville, outside the Christmas Family Home.

Characters

Abbie Adams - the Christmas family's next door neighbor (age 10 - 12, could be Aaron, a boy)

The Christmas Family*

December Christmas (or Mrs. C): the mother (mid 40s)
Merry Christmas: the oldest daughter (age 10 - 12)
Holly and Jolly Christmas: the twins (can be girls or boys age 6 - 8)
Happy Christmas: the older brother (age 12 - 14)
Whitey Christmas (or Mr. C): the father (mid 40s)

The cousins

(All choir members are "cousins." Everyone is dressed in outdoor Christmas clothing to fit your particular climate.)

Soloists:

Joy	Will	Don	Bell (#1)
Noel	Harold	Gloria	Bell (#2)
Star (#1)	Gaye	Star (#2)	Carol (#1)
Ken			Carol (#2)

*All speaking parts are divided among these characters, but many of their lines can be divided among the cousins listed as soloists, or other cousins given appropriate Christmas names, i.e., Candy, Frosty, Snowy, etc. In addition, Abbie's parts could be divided among two children, i.e., Abbie and Aaron.

Most solos are designated to a particular character, but can be assigned to any child.

Younger children (age 4 - 7) could enter before *Away in a Manger* as the "little cousins" with minor additions to the dialogue. They would stay on stage through the remainder of the musical, singing two songs and two reprises.

Set, Staging, and Props

The setting for *The Christmas Family Tree* is an outdoor scene, with or without snow. If you choose to paint a backdrop, the Christmas home would be in the background. The only set piece needed is a large, lighted Christmas tree. The tree can be placed centerstage or stage right, just don't let the tree conceal the children on risers. A variety of ornament patterns are included in this book and can be enlarged, copied to cardstock, and decorated by the children. These can make up the bulk of the ornaments on your tree, but feel free to add candy canes and garland or red ribbon. At the top of the tree should be an angel or star.

All staging directions are included within the script with the placement of the speakers indicated on the Staging Diagram. Choreography and additional staging suggestions are included in *The Christmas Family Tree* Instructional Video. *(Note: the props used in the choreography are shown on the instructional video.)*

The props you will need include:

- six foot step ladder
- ornaments reading Abraham, Rahab, Ruth, Boaz, Obed, Jesse, David, Josiah, and Mary & Joseph
- ornaments for all the Christmas cousins listed in the Cast of Characters
- a dog on a leash
- a large wicker laundry basket, with a pillow and blanket inside
- a baby or realistic looking doll
- a large family Bible

Stage Diagram

STAGE LEFT

STAGE RIGHT

UPSTAGE

DOWNSTAGE

RISERS

RISERS

AUDIENCE

AUDIENCE

Abbie Entrance

Cousins Entrance

Happy and Mr. C Entrance

Merry

Abbie

Mr. C
Mrs. C

Happy
Jolly

Holly

The Christmas Family Tree
(Intro)

Music by KATHIE HILL
Arranged by Chris Marion

*Dialogue on next page begins

8

(The cousins enter from stage right and left and/or through audience. There is a large Christmas tree center stage or stage right. Butted next to it is a 6 foot ladder upon which Mrs. C is perched at the top. Each child either hands Mrs. C an ornament or places an ornament on the tree before taking their places on risers.)

MRS. C: Come on, cousins. Let's decorate this tree. Here, I'll help you hang the ornaments.

MERRY: Be careful up on that ladder, Mother.

MRS. C: I will, I will. Have you invited our neighbor to the party.

MERRY: Not yet, but there she is, walking her dog. (*sound effect of a dog barking) I'll go ask her now.

(Merry approaches Abbie, crossing from stage left holding a dog on a leash.)

*The sound effect of a dog barking appears on the accompaniment CD at 71

MERRY: Abbie? Abbie Adams?

ABBIE: Yes?

MERRY: My name is Merry and I'm your new neighbor. You probably noticed we moved in last week.

ABBIE: (excited) Oh, yes. I see you're decorating the tree in your front yard.

MERRY: That's why I came over. I'd like to invite you to our family tree-trimming party.

ABBIE: Are all those kids in your family? Why, there're dozens of them!

MERRY: They're my cousins. Cousins by the dozens*, you might say!

(Abbie and Merry laugh together)

MRS. C: Merry Christmas! Merry Christmas!

ABBIE: And who's the lady with all the holiday spirit?

MERRY: Oh, that's my mother. She especially wants you to join us, Abbie.

ABBIE: Well, okay. Lemme put up the dog. I'll be right back. (**sound effect of a dog barking) (to dog as she moves stage left) Come on, Rocky.

MERRY: (calling to her) I'll wait here.

MRS. C: Merry Christmas! Merry Christmas!

(Abbie enters from stage left, without dog.)

*"Cousins by the dozens" for small choir and "cousins by the dozens and dozens" for larger choirs.

**The sound effect of a dog barking appears on the accompaniment CD at 72

Merry Christmas!

Words and Music by
KATHY HILL
Arranged by Chris Marion

name of Christ is heard, bring-ing joy to ev-'ry-one you're
one of them would hear, you'd get miles of smiles and e-ven

talk - ing to. Mer-ry
words of cheer.

D.S. al Coda

ABBIE: I'm ready, Merry

MERRY: Alright!

here. Mer-ry Christ-mas! Mer-ry Christ-mas! We

CODA

MERRY: Coming, Mother!

ABBIE: You mean she's been calling *you?*

MERRY: I'm afraid so.

ABBIE: That means your name is "Merry…"

MERRY: "Merry Christmas." I know it's not your usual last name. But we Christmases are quite proud of it. Holly, Jolly … come meet Abbie!

(Holly and Jolly rush from stage right to meet Abbie.)

ABBIE: Holly and … Jolly?

MERRY: The twins.

HOLLY: I'm Holly.

JOLLY: I'm Jolly.

HOLLY: Hi, Abbie.

JOLLY: Bye, Abbie.

(Holly and Jolly rush to the risers, hugging some cousins and shaking hands with others.)

MERRY: Pardon their rushing off. Our cousins have just arrived and the twins are excited to show them around.

MRS. C: *(from atop the ladder)* Merry Christmas! Would you help me down from this ladder, dear?

(Merry and Abbie walk toward ladder and steady it for Mrs. C.)

MERRY: Here I am. Be careful, Mother.

MRS. C: I always am, always am. *(seeing Abbie)* Ahh! This must be our famous next door neighbor. Christmas cousins, everyone! This is Abigail Adams, descendant of the founder of Adamsville!

COUSINS: Hi, Abbie. Hello. Glad to meet you. *(etc.)*

MERRY: Abbie, this is my mother, December Christmas. But you can just call her "Mrs. C."

ABBIE: Nice to meet you, Mrs. C. I see you're already familiar with our town's history.

MRS. C: I am, I am. You might as well know, I'm kind of a history buff. I even read a book on Adamsville before we moved here. I've always been interested in genealogies, family trees and the like. As a matter of fact, that's how we decorate our tree—to reflect the original Christmas family.

ABBIE: Really?

MRS. C: Speaking of family … do you have any brothers or sisters, Abbie?

ABBIE: No, ma'am. Just a dog.

MRS. C: Then you must make friends with the Christmas cousins. Why we've got cousins …

ABBIE: … by the dozens!

MRS. C: *(chuckling)* We do, we do!

MERRY: Do the cousins know about the surprise, Mother?

MRS. C: Well, it wouldn't be much of a surprise if they did, now would it? We'll just keep *that* a "mother-daughter" secret! *(to cousins)* Gather 'round the tree, everyone, and introduce yourselves to our new neighbor, Abbie Adams.

The Christmas Family Tree Medley

Arranged by Chris Marion

Arrangement © copyright 1997 Van Ness Press, Inc. (ASCAP).
Distributed by GENEVOX (a div. of GMG), Nashville, TN 37234.

MRS. C: Let's see. We'll start with Merry, whom you've already met, and my oldest nephew, Ken.

*"We Wish You a Merry Christmas," Anonymous.
**The words that appear in bold italic print should be sung (or spoken) by the named character.

Hap-py New Year! Good tid-ings we bring to you and your *Ken.* We

wish you a *Mer-ry Christ-mas* and a Hap-py New Year! Good

tid-ings we bring to you and your *Ken.* We wish you a *Mer-ry Christ-mas* and a

MRS. C: Of course, you need to hear from the
twins and some of the cousins.

Hap-py New Year!

Done.

*"Deck the Halls with Boughs of Holly," Words Traditional; Music Old Welsh tune.

20

MRS. C: Abbie, I'd like you to meet another one of the nephews.

fa, la, la, la, la, la, la, la, la.

*Hark! the Har - old an - gels sing, ___ "Glo - ry to the

ABBIE: Hi, Harold, and this is...
MRS. C: my niece.

new - born King." _____

**How great our Joy!

*"Hark! The Herald Angels Sing," Words by CHARLES WESLEY; Music by FELIX MENDELSSOHN.
**"How Great Our Joy," Traditional German Carol.

21

*"Angels We Have Heard on High," Word and music Traditional French Carol.

63
o'er the plains; And the moun - tains in re-ply

66
Ech - o - ing their joy - ous strains. *Glo* -

69
ri - a

MRS. C: *(chuckles)* Gloria is the best singer
in the whole family.

72
Glo -

*"The First Nowell," Words and music Traditional English Carol.

24

MRS. C: You know, Abbie, we have so many cousins, some of them even have the same names. For example:

MRS. C: But this cousin is the most flamboyant!

*"We Three Kings of Orient Are," Words and music by JOHN HENRY HOPKINS, JR.

26

MRS. C: Come on everybody, gather 'round the tree. Abbie, Merry, Holly, and Jolly over here. And, of course, all the Christmas cousins.

*"The Christmas Family Tree," Words and music by KATHIE HILL.

MRS. C: Happy Christmas!

ABBIE: *(enthusiastically)* Happy Christmas to you, Mrs. C!

MRS. C: No, no, Abbie. I was calling my son, Happy. Happy Christmas.

(Enter Happy from stage right. He crosses to join them while Merry moves toward Holly and Jolly, who are starting to climb the ladder.)

HAPPY: Hey, Mom.

MRS. C: Happy, this is Abbie. *(to Merry)* Merry, get Holly and Jolly down from that ladder!

MERRY: *(moving to the ladder)* Yes, ma'am.

ABBIE: Happy to meet you … Happy. *(being friendly)* And Merry Christmas!

MERRY: *(yelling from ladder)* Over here, Abbie!

ABBIE: *(totally confused)* Oh, dear. This is confusing.

HAPPY: Hey, Mom. Where's Dad?

(Merry, Holly, and Jolly move back to center stage.)

MRS. C: *(winking to Merry)* Oh, he's coming, Happy.

MERRY: And bringing the best Christmas present of all!

MRS. C: Now, Merry Christmas … that's our secret!

HAPPY: What's a secret?

MRS. C: Let's just say, "Good things come to those who wait." They do, they do!

HAPPY: Whatever you say, Mom.

MRS. C: Abbie, I'm so glad you've joined us. Being from such a long line of Adams, you might find it interesting to read some of the names on our Christmas family tree.

ABBIE: *(looking closely at one of the ornaments)* So that's what's written on your ornaments! The names of all the Christmas cousins!

MRS. C: Oh, not all of them. Some have yet to join the *original* Christmas family.

ABBIE: The *original* Christmas family?

MERRY: The family of faith.

MRS. C: That's right. Are you familiar with the Bible, Abbie?

ABBIE: Oh, sure. We've got a big family Bible on the coffee table. *(proudly)* I even know all the ancestors written in the front. *(as if suddenly realizing)* But, I've never actually read the book.

MRS. C: Well, then many of these names may be unfamiliar to you. Tell her more, Happy

(Happy moves to the tree and takes off an ornament.)

HAPPY: Abbie, the first ornament we place on the tree is always for Abraham ... because that's were the family of faith began.

ABBIE: Pardon me, but wasn't Adam the first man?

MRS. C: You know more about the Bible than you thought! Adam *was* the first man. But Adam and his wife, Eve, disobeyed God. Then, instead of having the faith that God would forgive them, they hid from God, and blamed their mistakes on each other. And because of their deception, Adam and Eve could no longer be a part of the home God had made for them.

ABBIE: In the Garden of Eden?

MERRY: That's right. So years later, God chose Abraham to be the father of a new nation, known as God's chosen people.

ABBIE: But what did Abraham have that no one else had?

HAPPY: Hey, cousins! What did Abraham have?

COUSINS: Faith!

MERRY: Abraham's faith made him available *to* God to do great things *for* God.

ABBIE: But, isn't faith just believing there *is* a God?

HAPPY: It's that, but a whole lot more, Abbie. Can I tell you how someone explained faith to me?

ABBIE: Sure.

F-A-I-T-H

Words and Music by
KATHIE HILL
Arranged by Chris Marion

HAPPY: Abraham had real "f-a-i-t-h" …

HOLLY: and so should "y-o-u" …

JOLLY: and "m-e!"

MERRY: It's twin time!

(all chuckle)

MRS. C: Holly and Jolly. Tell Abbie how Abraham proved his faith.

HOLLY: God told Abraham to leave his home in the land of Ur and live in a far off land called Canaan.

JOLLY: 'Course, he'd never even heard of Canaan, but by faith, he went!

ABBIE: Then what happened?

HOLLY: God said He would give Abraham and his wife, Sarah, a son.

JOLLY: 'Course, by then, they were both senior citizens, but by faith, they believed and God gave them a son!

ABBIE: Then what happened?

HOLLY: God asked Abraham to offer up that son, Isaac, as a sacrifice.

JOLLY: And by faith, he did.

ABBIE: Then what happened?

HOLLY: God spared the boy when He saw that Abraham's faith was real.

ABBIE: (thinking to herself, remembering) Faith. For all I trust him.

MERRY: That's right, Abbie.

ABBIE: So, Merry? Who else beside Abraham is in the original Christmas family.

MERRY: (taking an ornament from the tree) My favorite is Rahab, because we read about her faith in three books of the Bible; Joshua, Matthew, and Hebrews.

ABBIE: How did she trust God?

MERRY: Rahab risked her life by hiding Joshua's spies.

ABBIE: Joshua?

HAPPY: You know. Joshua fought the battle of Jericho!

ABBIE: (embarrassed) No. I don't know.

The Battle of Jericho Revisited

(Underscore)

*Dialogue on following page begins.

Music Traditional
Arranged by Chris Marion

MERRY: Oh, but that's one of the Bible's best examples of faith. You see, Joshua was one of God's greatest leaders and when God told him to take the city of Jericho, He gave Joshua some rather odd instructions.

ABBIE: Odd?

HAPPY: God told Joshua to march his army around Jericho seven times … then blow the ram's horn, shout, and the city walls would fall for the Lord.

ABBIE: So, where does Rahab fit into the story?

MERRY: Before Joshua brought his whole army, he sneaked two spies into Jericho, just to check things out. When they needed a place to hide, Rahab risked her life by hiding Joshua's men—right under the noses of the enemy.

ABBIE: Were they caught?

HAPPY: Nope. When the coast was clear, Rahab let down a long red rope for Joshua's men to escape.

MERRY: And when Joshua's army returned, his soldiers knew to protect Rahab because they could still see the long red cord.

MRS. C: I like to remember it as her "hope on a rope."

HAPPY: *(teasing)* Oh, Mom!

MRS. C: I do, I do!

ABBIE: *(chuckling)* Wow, Rahab must have been a very brave woman.

MRS. C: She was, she was. And much of Joshua's victory at Jericho is due to Rahab's faith.

MERRY: Hey, to understand her faith better, how about we "revisit" the battle of Jericho?

COUSINS: I love this story. Let's tell it! I wanna be Joshua. *(etc.)*

The Battle of Jericho Revisited

Words and Music Traditional
Additional Words by KATHIE HILL
Arranged by Chris Marion

40

42

COUSINS: That was fun! I love that story. Way to go, Merry. *(etc.)*

ABBIE: That's a great story, Mrs. C. But what does the battle of Jericho have to do with Christmas?

MRS. C: Well, according to the gospel of Matthew, there had to be a Rahab before there could be a Savior.

ABBIE: How's that?

(Five cousins bring out five over-sized ornaments)

MRS. C: Here, we'll use these five ornaments to show you.

(Cousins line up stage right of Mrs. C with Rahab first, then Boaz, Obed, Jesse, and lastly, David's ornament.)

MRS. C: Rahab had a son named Boaz, a grandson named Obed, a great-grandson named Jesse, and a great-great-grandson named David.

ABBIE: You really are a history buff, Mrs. C!

MRS. C: I am, I am. And does the name David mean anything to you?

ABBIE: *(thinking)* Not really.

HAPPY: Well, Abbie … even if David doesn't ring a bell, he sure could play the harp.

(Cousins giggle.)

ABBIE: Oh! *That* David.

MRS. C: Yes. And just as you're a direct descendant of Archibald Adams, the prophets said Jesus would be a direct descendant of King David. *(pointing out the Rahab ornament)* So Jesus' family tree records both great-great Granny Rahab and great-grandma Ruth. (pointing out the Ruth ornament.)

MERRY: Here. Read Ruth's ornament. *(handing it to Abbie)*

ABBIE: *(reading)* "May the Lord deal with me … if anything but death separates you and me." That's so romantic, Mrs. C. Did Ruth say that to her husband?

MRS. C: No. Ruth made that promise to her mother-in-law, Naomi. In fact, it's quite a beautiful story.

ABBIE: Tell it, Mrs. C.

COUSINS: Yeah. We wanna hear it again. Go ahead. *(etc.)*

True to You
(Underscore)

Dialogue on following page begins.

Music by KATHIE HILL
Arranged by Chris Marion

MRS. C: Well, the Bible says a famine, in the land of Judah, forced
           Naomi, her husband, and children to live in a foreign land
           called Moab. There, her son married a Moabite woman
           named Ruth. When the famine killed Naomi's husband
           and son, Naomi thought Ruth would be happier to stay in
           Moab and find another husband among her own people.

ABBIE: I can just imagine Ruth was young and pretty. Don't you
           think so, Mrs. C.?

MRS. C: I suspect so, Abbie. But pretty is as pretty does. And Ruth
           did a pretty remarkable thing. She had grown to love
           Naomi so much, Ruth refused to leave her mother-in-law.
           Better still, she had grown to love Naomi's God.

MERRY: So tell what happened back in Judah!

MRS. C: Well, Naomi went back to her home in Bethlehem and
           Ruth did everything she could to provide for her. And
           when Ruth was gathering leftover grain the the field of
           Naomi's cousin Boaz, Boaz was so impressed with her
           loyalty that he fell in love with Ruth and married her.

ABBIE: *That* is romantic!

MRS. C: Uh, huh. And that is how Ruth became the
           great-grandmother of King David and a pretty important
           person in the original Christmas family.

ABBIE: I'd say that's better than marrying into the Adams family!

(They all laugh.)

ABBIE: Is that a true story, Mrs. C?

MRS. C: Why, yes Abbie. All the stories in the Bible are true. And
           all the stories have a lesson for us—this one being that
           loyalty to God is always rewarded.

True to You

Words and Music by
KATHIE HILL
Arranged by Chris Marion

54

MRS. C: Ruth's words to Naomi are some of the most beautiful in the Bible, and what better gift can you give at Christmas than the gift of loyalty to your family, your friends, and especially, to God.

HAPPY: Speaking of gifts, where's Dad? We'll be finished trimming the tree if he doesn't come soon.

MRS. C: Just hold on, Happy. He'll be here any minute.

MERRY: Can I tell Happy the surprise, Mother?

COUSINS: Yeah, come on and tell us. A surprise? What is it? (etc.)

MRS. C: (sternly) Now, now. Remember, good things happen to those who *wait*.

(All groan in disappointment)

ABBIE: So, Happy. Where's King David's ornament on the Christmas family tree?

HAPPY: (pointing to a lower branch) Right here on this bough, Abbie. Abraham started the family of faith when he was chosen by God. Rahab connected herself to the family through her bravery and Ruth was adopted into the family of faith through her loyalty. That brings us to King David, from whose family Jesus would be born.

ABBIE: What made David so special?

HAPPY: The Bible says David was a man after God's own heart.

MERRY: That means he loved God more than anything.

HAPPY: And even though David made some big mistakes, he was always quick to admit his sins and ask God's forgiveness. So, one day, the King of kings would be born in David's hometown of Bethlehem.

MERRY: The Messiah, a descendant of King David, just as scripture had promised.

Once in Royal David's City

Words by
CECIL F. ALEXANDER

Music by
HENRY J. GAUNTLETT
Arranged by Chris Marion

Arrangement © copyright 1997 Van Ness Press, Inc. (ASCAP).
Distributed by GENEVOX (a div. of GMG), Nashville, TN 37234.

56

58

60

HAPPY:	Can you believe the same David who started out as a shepherd boy ended up a king and part of Jesus' family?
ABBIE:	Who else do you guys like in the Christmas family tree?
MRS. C:	Tell her, Holly and Jolly.
HOLLY:	*(bringing an ornament)* No doubt about it.
JOLLY:	Josiah!
MERRY:	Once again … it's twin time!

(All giggle.)

ABBIE:	Why do you like … Josiah?
HOLLY and JOLLY:	He was just our size!
MRS. C:	Josiah became king of Judah when he was only eight … just about the same age as the twins.
ABBIE:	But, how could an eight-year-old be in charge of a whole nation?
HOLLY:	Because he asked God for wisdom.
JOLLY:	'Course, God gave Josiah wisdom because he "turned to the Lord, with all his heart."
HOLLY:	This little king gave God a whole lot of Josiah,
JOLLY:	… and got a whole lot of wisdom in return!

Wholly His

Words and Music by
KATHIE HILL
Arranged by Chris Marion

66

ABBIE: So were all the kings after David as good as King Josiah?

MRS. C: No, Abbie. Just like in any family, they had some bad apples in the family tree. Kings who were impatient and took matters into their own hands instead of trusting God. But, in Josiah's case, I'd have to admit "good *kings* happen to those who wait."

(*Cousins chuckle and groan.*)

HAPPY: Speaking of waiting, are you sure we should finish the tree without Dad?

COUSINS: Where's Uncle Whitey? Why isn't he here? Where is he? (*etc.*)

MRS. C: There's no need to worry now, cousins. I know he wouldn't want us to wait on him.

HAPPY: But, what kind of present would keep him this long?

MERRY: A very wonderful present!

MRS. C: Now, Merry Christmas! Don't spoil the surprise.

(*Enter Mr. Christmas carrying a large basket.*)

MR. C: That's right, Merry. If God's children waited two thousand years from Abraham to Jesus, you can surely wait a few more minutes for *your* Christmas surprise.

MERRY: It's Daddy!

COUSINS: Look, it's Uncle Whitey! What's he got? He's carrying something. (*etc.*)

(*Mr. C gives Mrs. C a peck on the cheek.*)

MR. C: Hello, children … cousins!

MERRY: Daddy, this is our neighbor, Abbie Adams. Abbie, this is Mrs. C's other half … Mr. C.

ABBIE: Glad to meet you and Merry Chris … I mean Happy Chris … (*confused*) I mean … Hi!

MR. C: (*chuckles*) Hi to you, too, Abbie.

HOLLY: What've you been up to and what's in that big basket, Daddy?

JOLLY: Mother said there'd be a present!

HAPPY: Yeah, and I think the present is *present!*

(They giggle.)

COUSINS: What could it be? It's such a big basket! Now, that's a surprise. Tell us what it is. *(etc.)*

MR. C: I didn't mean to make you wait. But, now that the wait is over, I have the most wonderful way to tell the Christmas story.

ABBIE: The Christmas story?

(Dialogue continues on next page.)

Away in a Manger
(Underscore)

Music by JAMES R. MURRAY
Arranged by Chris Marion

Arrangement © copyright 1997 Van Ness Press, Inc. (ASCAP).
Distributed by GENEVOX (a div. of GMG), Nashville, TN 37234.

72

MERRY: Yes. We always end our tree-trimming with the Christmas story from the Bible.

MRS. C: The Christmas story is a beautiful picture of the faithfulness of two young people and the blessing that came through their obedience to God.

COUSINS: I love this part! The Christmast story. Tell it, Uncle Whitey. Shh … he's about to begin. *(etc.)*

MR. C: This is how the birth of Jesus Christ came about. His mother Mary was pledged to be married to Joseph, but before they came together she was found to be with child through the Holy Spirit. Because Joseph, her husband, was a righteous man and did not want to expose her to public disgrace, he had in mind to divorce her quietly.

But after he had considered this, an angel of the Lord appeared to him in a dream and said, "Joseph, son of David, do not be afraid to take Mary home as your wife, because what is conceived in her is from the Holy Spirit. She will give birth to a son, and you are to give Him the name … Jesus, because He will save His people from their sins." *(Matt. 1:18-25)*

Away in a Manger

Arranged by Chris Marion

*"Away in a Manger," Words Anonymous; Music by JAMES R. MURRAY

*"Away in a Manger," Words Anonymous; Music by JOHN THOMAS McFARLAND.

MR. C: All this took place to fulfill what the Lord had said through the prophet; "the virgin will be with child and will give birth to a Son, and they will call Him Immanuel" which means, "God with us."

*"Away in a Manger," Words JOHN THOMAS MCFARLAND; Music by JAMES R. MURRAY

78

(*sound effect of a baby cry)

HAPPY: What in the world? Where did that noise come from?

(Mrs. C lifts a small baby from the large basket and displays her proudly.)

MRS. C: (offended) Noise? That beautiful *music* came from Angela.
           Angela Faith Christmas.

(Mr. C places his arm around Mrs. C as they gaze at the baby.)

COUSINS: Look at the baby. She's beautiful. How precious! (etc.)

HOLLY: Is there another one in that basket?

JOLLY: (lifting the blanket and peering into the basket) Yeah. Is it twin
           time?

MRS. C: (chuckling) No … there's just one of her!

MERRY: But, where did she come from?

MR. C: From the airport. And before that, from across the ocean.

MRS. C: Christmas family, meet our newest member, our adopted
           daughter, Angela Faith.

COUSINS: Hello, Angela Faith. How do you do? Look at our new
           cousin. (etc.)

HOLLY: Adopted?

JOLLY: Yeah. No one told us you and Mom were going to adopt a
           baby!

MERRY: That's because it was a secret! Remember? She said, "Good
           things come to those who wait."

HAPPY: But this isn't *good*. This is *great*! Can I hold her, Mom?

MRS. C: Of course, Happy. Be careful now.

(Happy takes the baby from Mrs. C as Mr. C, Merry, Holly, and Jolly and several
cousins gush over the baby quietly.)

ABBIE: Angela Faith. That's such a pretty name, Mrs. C. And exactly
           what we've been talking about! The faithful things people did
           to become part of God's family.

MRS. C: Yes, Abbie. But after Jesus was born, it wasn't faithful deeds
           that brought a person into His family. It was Jesus'
           faithfulness.

ABBIE: What did Jesus do?

*The sound effect of a baby crying appears on the accompaniment CD at 73

Everyone, Everywhere Come
(Underscore)

*Dialogue on following page begins.

Music by KATHIE HILL
Arranged by Chris Marion

MRS. C: As God's Son, Jesus lived a perfect life. But, He knew we couldn't be perfect, so He died on a cross to pay the price for our mistakes. Then he rose from the grave to prepare a home for us in heaven.

ABBIE: That *is* a faithful deed.

MRS. C: Yes. And next to that, anything we might do seems useless in comparison.

ABBIE: So how can we be a part of God's family?

MRS. C: By having faith in Jesus.

ABBIE: Faith. For all I trust Him.

MRS. C: That's right. Just as we received Angela into our family, Jesus receives anyone who comes to Him by faith. Whether you're an Adams or a nobody, Jesus longs to adopt you into His family of faith.

ABBIE: So, how can I do that?

MRS. C: Well, think about what you've learned today. Tell God you want to be a part of the family He started with Abraham. If you're afraid, ask for bravery, like Rahab. Tell Him you want to be loyal, like Ruth, and, like David, ask God to forgive your sins. Then pray for wisdom, like Josiah and try to be obedient, like Mary and Joseph.

ABBIE: Will you help me do that?

MRS. C: Of course. Let's find a quiet place to pray.

(Abbie and Mrs. C move stage right and kneel to pray. They should return centerstage by the end of "Everyone, Everywhere Come.")

Everyone, Everywhere Come

Words and Music by
KATHIE HILL
Arranged by Chris Marion

82

*"Softly and Tenderly," Words and music by WILL L. THOMPSON

84

ABBIE: It feels like I've come home—even though I live right next door!

MR. C: You have come home, Abbie. To the family of faith.

ABBIE: And even though I'm still an Adams ... now *I'm* part of the Christmas family tree, right?

MRS. C: That's right!

MERRY: *(excited)* We need to put your ornament on the tree, Abbie.

ABBIE: Yeah. And one for Angela Faith.

HAPPY: *(holding the baby)* No. She'll place her name on the tree when she asks Jesus into her heart, just like you did.

HOLLY: Until then, let's make Abbie's ornament really pretty.

JOLLY: With lots of glitter!

ABBIE: *(excited)* I get to sign my name!

(Abbie, Merry, Holly, and Jolly run stage right to make the ornament.)

HAPPY: Here, Mom. You hold the baby while I climb the ladder to hang Abbie's ornament.

(Happy gives the baby to Mrs. C and climbs the ladder.)

MR. C: *(stroking the baby's head)* Well, Mrs. C. Don't you think this has been the best Christmas ever?

MRS. C: I do, I do!

(Abbie hands her ornament to Happy to hang on the tree during "The Christmas Family Tree Reprise.")

The Christmas Family Tree Reprise

Words and Music by
KATHIE HILL
Arranged by Chris Marion

Brightly (♩ = 108)

CHOIR

Gath - er 'round the tree, the Christ - mas fam - 'ly tree. Where love a - bounds and joy - ous sounds fill the win - ter air as we wel - come all those here to the

88

An instrumental version of "Merry Christmas" appears on the accompaniment CD at **70**

(Cast should take bows during the instrumental reprise in this order: Mr. C, Holly and Jolly, Happy, Merry, Mrs. C with baby, then Abbie. Cast should sing on the last chorus, waving at the spoken ending.)

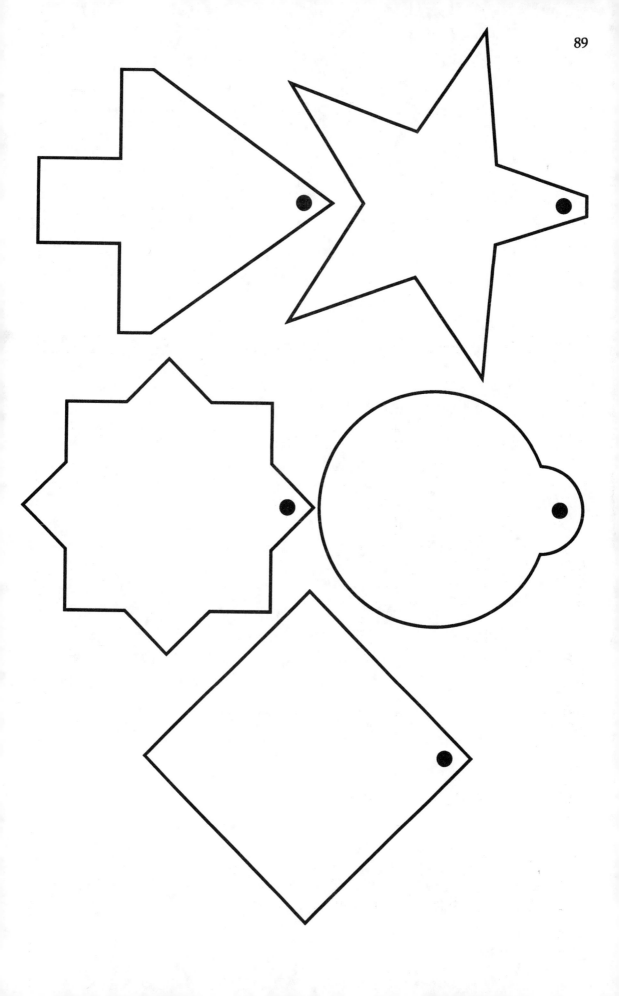